TOTTENHAM'S TROJAN HORSE?

A Tale of Stadium-led Regeneration in North London

Dr Mark Panton
and Amanda Lillywhite

Part of the plan for the *High Road West* area of Tottenham in North London is that the entrance to White Hart Lane Station will be moved southwards, then a swathe of buildings will be demolished to create a paved walkway lined by new buildings. The walkway will link the station to the new home of Tottenham Hotspur Football Club.

TOTTENHAM HIGH ROAD

SITE OF PROPOSED WALKWAY

If the walkway proposals go ahead social housing, private residences, many shops, small and medium-sized businesses plus a library will be demolished by 2022. This includes a total of 297 properties in Ermine House, Charles House and Moselle House on the Love Lane Estate, 2-32 & 3-89 Whitehall Street, 4-18 Brereton Road, 2-28 Orchard Place, 9-39 White Hart Lane, Kathleen Ferrier Road and 731-759 Tottenham High Road.

A huge area opposite the new stadium would be cleared away to make it easier for fans to reach the new stadium. Existing privately owned businesses replaced by franchises and many current residents cleansed from the area because they can't afford the new rents or property prices. All of this achieved through so-called "decanting" and the use of Compulsory Purchase Orders.

What are Compulsory Purchase Orders?

Compulsory Purchase Orders allow public bodies such as councils to force property owners to sell up if their home or building obstructs a regeneration project or it's for the "greater public good" and not for private gain. This can enable councils to buy up all the land and property in a given area if they are able to prove the development will be of public benefit. An act of Parliament in 2004 altered the definition of "public benefit" by placing far greater importance on the potential economic gains of a big new scheme, rather than taking into account the impact on individuals or communities.

Families who have lived in Tottenham for generations and who hoped to see their children grow up on the same streets will have to move away.

We live above our shop with our children and completely re-built our garden for them. We've just finished refurbishing the shop, not just a lick of paint, refurbishing everything. We had a new roof and solar panels put on.

We've invested time, money, blood, sweat, everything. Tears. Arguments, disputes, agreements. We've put everything into this business.

This is a case of a very large land-owner wanting control of the retail area opposite a new stadium. That's what it's about.

The Housing Question

The growth of the big modern cities gives the land in certain areas, particularly in those which are centrally situated, an artificially and colossally increasing value; the buildings erected on these areas depress this value instead of increasing it, because they no longer belong to the changed circumstances. They are pulled down and replaced by others. This takes place above all with workers houses which are centrally situated and whose rents, even with the greatest overcrowding, can never, or only very slowly, increase above a certain maximum. They are pulled down and in their stead shops, warehouses and public buildings are erected, (From an article by Frederick Engels written in 1872).

The way I've read the research, regeneration should help the community, especially Tottenham. Tottenham's had rough times. All they're doing is moving the social housing out and moving all the little businesses that have been here for donkeys years out and giving it over to developers.

I've lived in Tottenham all my life. I have never been scared, not until I saw these plans. The uncertainty and strain it has put on our family and neighbours is awful.

To understand how this situation came about we need to go back to...

BARNET

ENFIELD

HARINGEY

Tottenham.

REDBRIDGE

WALTHAM
FOREST

CAMDEN

HACKNEY

...2010

NEWHAM

CITY

TOWER
HAMLETS

WESTMINSTER

THAMES RIVER

SOUTHWARK

GREENWICH

Tottenham Hotspur FC was at the time, and still is, the largest landowner in the area and a significant local employer. Throughout this period it has been an important provider of community outreach work such as health and sport education in it's stadium and at schools. In 2016 it was the 12th richest football club in the world and has played in Northumberland Park, Tottenham since 1888.

Tottenham is in the London Borough of Haringey. Some residents near the stadium were in 2010, and still are, amongst those on the lowest incomes in England.

CROYDON

BROMLEY

By 2010 Haringey Council had already been in discussion with Tottenham Hotspur FC for a number of years about planning permission for a new stadium and associated developments to be built by the football club.

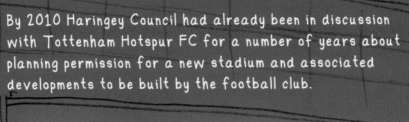

WELCOME TO TOTTENHAM HOTSPUR

Tottenham Hotspur have been trying to buy up the leases and freeholds opposite the stadium for years.

They've also been using Bermuda registered companies to buy properties.

But the council said there is absolutely no possibility of them going across the other side of Tottenham High Road.

In 2010 Haringey granted Tottenham Hotspur FC planning permission for their proposed developments that included £16,436,000 of Section 106 commitments. Also, half of the proposed 200 housing units to be built on the site of the old stadium were to be classified as affordable housing.

Failure is not an option, we will find a way to get this stadium built. We don't have a time limit because we have to be realistic.

Daniel Levy, Chairman, Tottenham Hotspur FC

This whole project will act as a catalyst for regeneration in this part of London.

Councillor Alan Strickland, Cabinet Member for Regeneration, Haringey

Is affordable housing really affordable?

The government's definition of affordable renting is that homes should cost no more than 80% of the average local market rent. For home ownership, it is a little less clear-cut. The government states that affordable housing must be provided at a level at which the mortgage payments on the property should be more than would be paid in rent on council housing, but below market levels. Some London boroughs have opposed the provision of affordable rent on the basis that it is not affordable for the majority of the borough's residents. It has been argued that secure, low rent social homes are being rapidly replaced by far more expensive, insecure properties with dire implications for low income tenants in London.

What are Section 106 commitments?

Planning obligations under Section 106 of the Town and Country Planning Act 1990 are a mechanism which makes a development proposal acceptable in planning terms. They are focused on mitigation of the impact of development and are also referred to as "developer contributions". They are often used to secure affordable housing, and to secure financial contributions towards transport infrastructure. Since 2015 local authorities have been required to ensure that the combined total impact of such requests does not threaten the viability of development sites.

Locally listed buildings were carefully preserved in plans for the new stadium in 2010 because earlier proposals that had required their demolition had been rejected.

Tottenham Hotspur FC were unhappy with the Section 106 commitments they were required to make for their new stadium. They commissioned a report which concluded that the project was not financially viable; then Haringey Council commissioned their own report that agreed there were significant viability issues. The full reports have never been made public.

Tottenham Hotspur FC put pressure on Haringey Council. They announced a bid to take over the London Olympic Stadium after the 2012 Olympics. This would mean a move out of Tottenham and the borough of Haringey to Stratford in the borough of Newham 6 miles away.

TOTTENHAM

Our proposal will retain around £420m worth of the Olympic Stadium, and we will re-use or recycle the £80m that will be dismantled with zero landfill. It is also important to remember that two thirds of the Olympic Stadium, under the original legacy plan, was to be dismantled - it was not designed to be a permanent structure. Recent scaremongering conveniently forgets this fact.

Daniel Levy, Chairman,
Tottenham Hotspur FC

STRATFORD

THAMES
RIVER

Residents, local businesses - most people with any kind of stake in Tottenham - were devastated by news of the bid. They had strong ties to the football club. The stadium brought in revenue, created jobs and it was a local landmark. Fans were equally upset. Many of them and their parents and grandparents before, had gone to matches at White Hart Lane since early childhood.

I'm a Spurs fan and when they said they were going to go to Stratford, all the shopkeepers had a petition. Because we think, how are you going to have all those Spurs fans going in to West Ham territory, their rivals, and they know they are going to lose a lot of fans at the same time as doing that. But we want them to stay.

Tottenham Resident and Shopkeeper

It isn't just that selfishly we want to stay more or less where we are, but there is a genuine feeling that if ever there was an area of London that needed a major new development it's Tottenham.

South London based Spurs Fan

Then, on 6 August 2011, a riot devastated a stretch of Tottenham High Road.

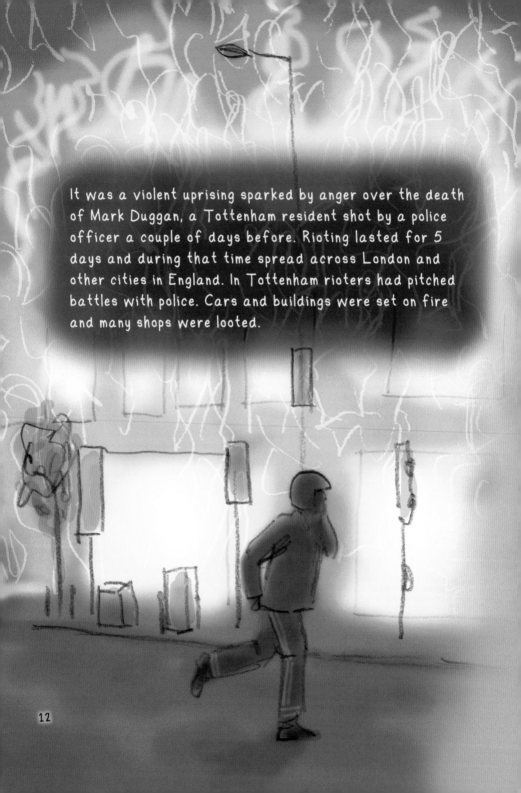

It was a violent uprising sparked by anger over the death of Mark Duggan, a Tottenham resident shot by a police officer a couple of days before. Rioting lasted for 5 days and during that time spread across London and other cities in England. In Tottenham rioters had pitched battles with police. Cars and buildings were set on fire and many shops were looted.

Immediately after the riots, a demonstration was called by anti-cuts activists and local Turkish groups. About 3,000 people marched from Dalston in Hackney to Tottenham Town Hall under the banner of "Give our Kids a Future". It was a really powerful statement saying that what we want is improved community facilities and public services and community-led regeneration in Hackney and Tottenham.

Dave Morris,
Tottenham Resident
and Community Activist

A number of reports were published that explored the reasons for rioting in Tottenham. It was felt that there were underlying factors such as poverty and inequality. One of the reports, *It Took Another Riot*, saw property development as a solution to many of the problems. The report was commissioned by the Mayor of London at the time, Boris Johnson, carried out by property developer, Sir Stuart Lipton, and backed by Haringey Council.

In January 2012
Boris Johnson announced...

£41,345,000 funding to regenerate, transform and restore pride to Tottenham.

But the money was only meant to kickstart projects, the main bulk of the funding would have to be found elsewhere.

13

Like all councils at the time Haringey had been under huge financial pressure. After a general election in 2010 the Conservative and Liberal Democrat parties had formed a coalition government and brought in an austerity budget resulting in huge public service cuts across the UK. In 2011 planning policy was also changed:

We'll remove the requirement forcing builders to include low cost housing to get planning permission for new developments.

Developers will no longer have to wait five years to apply to change affordable housing requirements if they are making sites unviable.

Councils will be put into "special measures" if they fail to respond speedily to planning permission requests.

Nick Clegg, Liberal Democrat Leader, 2007-2015

David Cameron, Prime Minister, 2010-2016

Dave Morris, Tottenham Resident and Community Activist

Councils might get a Section 106 contribution which they can use for local services, schools and so on. But the other part of the equation is the government starving public services of the funding they need. All councils are having to make massive cuts when they should be getting increases for our vital public services. This leads to top-down, profit-led developments and massive demolitions. So really it's a kind of perfect storm of attacks on the ability of the community to get the kind of development and services and facilities we need.

What is an Austerity Budget?

Austerity is a political-economic term referring to policies that aim to reduce government budget deficits through spending cuts and tax increases, or a combination of both. The coalition government's 2010 austerity budget impacted in three connected ways in Haringey:

(1) economic concerns were prioritised by central government leading to extensive local government budget cuts;

(2) a reliance by Haringey on private developers to assist with regeneration; and

(3) a subsequent loss of local accountability.

In February 2012 Haringey knocked £16 million off Tottenham Hotspur FC's Section 106 commitments reducing it to £477,000. The new stadium and associated developments would cover the same area as before but 85 housing units were added to make a total of 285, all of which could be sold on the open market and housing that was deemed to be affordable had disappeared.

...the council obviously wants Tottenham Hotspur Football Club to stay and maybe that's why, from the Section 106 point of view, various sweeteners...

Haringey Councillor

If it accepted the new terms the football club would save money from the huge reduction in their Section 106 commitments and make a lot more money from the sale of housing.

In February 2011 Tottenham Hotspur FC had lost out to West Ham on the Olympic stadium bid. Though the site in Tottenham was now their only option they gave no public reaction to the deal offered by Haringey because they had a problem that could derail the whole project. The new stadium was to be built on a site that only partially overlapped the site of the old stadium. A small family-run business, Archway Metal, currently stood in the centre of the proposed new pitch. Archway Metal was refusing to bow to pressure to sell-up and move, so Tottenham Hotspur and Haringey council were in the process of obtaining a Compulsory Purchase Order.

The owner of Archway Metal said:

It's really difficult. I've always been a Tottenham fan and so are two of my brothers. We used to have a box there and I remember going to watch in the days Osvaldo Ardiles was a player.

The club has been going for a long time and it doesn't change my love for the club. But the ownership is different and so you find yourself having to distinguish between the two.

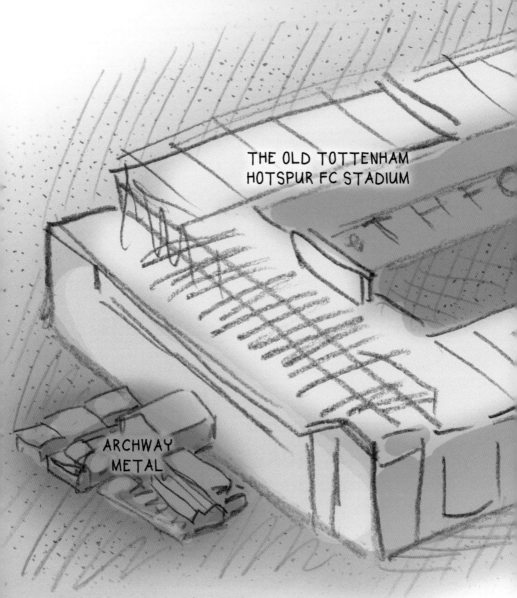

THE OLD TOTTENHAM
HOTSPUR FC STADIUM

ARCHWAY
METAL

Tottenham Hotspur FC's development plans were in stalemate,
but, helped by funding received from the Mayor of London,
Haringey Council was able to put together its own regeneration
plans. In July 2012 Haringey presented their ideas to the public
in a glossy brochure *A Plan for Tottenham*.

A Plan for Tottenham outlined massive regeneration plans for the area. The proposed developments were estimated to create up to 10,000 new homes, 5,000 new jobs and almost a million square feet of employment and commercial space.

This brochure sets out how we will increase the pace of Tottenham's transformation for the better. It is rightly an ambitious programme of change. We have to ensure that we set the bar high. My commitment is to do all that we can to deliver against our ambition.

Councillor Claire Kober,
Leader of Haringey Council

I want to see the area regenerated with the support of the people who live and work there, which I know is the ambition of the council too.

Daniel Levy, Chairman,
Tottenham Hotspur FC

Boris Johnson,
Mayor of London 2008-2016

We have long said we could only invest in the area if we could see our commitment supported by others and that there was a real need to maximise the regeneration benefits and lift the wider area.

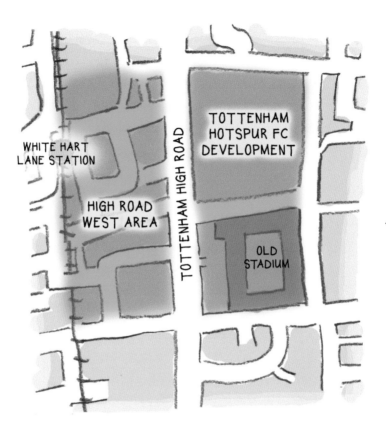

There were few details about what was actually planned. However it was clear that there would be huge change and it seemed that residents and small business owners would have very little influence in the decision making.

Realising that they would need to combine their voices in order to be heard, thirty community groups gathered at a public conference on 6 April 2013 to launch a Community Charter and form a network to be called...

Just going to the first Our Tottenham meeting was encouraging, supportive, because there are people out there who care and I thought we might just have to keep it amongst the parade of shops here, but we are supporting the cause of Our Tottenham and Our Tottenham are supporting our cause because it's all inter-linked.

We've started to overcome the kind of isolation and fragmentation of a whole range of different groups and campaigns.

People want to defend what they have got that is good, to slow things down that are proposed that are bad and hopefully stop them and to create or improve existing neighbourhoods that need improving.

TOTTENHAM

Our Tottenham Aims

We call on local people to campaign to defend our communities and to speak out for our real needs. Let's take action to...

* Defend community facilities.
* Stand up for decent and affordable housing for all.
* Support the local economy.
* Promote quality design and respect for heritage.
* Improve the street environment.
* Support youth voices, services and facilities.
* Defend and expand good public services.
* Work towards environmental sustainability.
* Empower our communities.
* Develop local community plans.

We're not against development, but we want it done properly. We're against the way the consultation's been held.

We think it should be done like Our Tottenham. It should be with the community and for the community.

A month later the details of *A Plan for Tottenham* started to be revealed.

21

The residents and business owners who received a *High Road West* consultation pack from Haringey Council for their area, and could understand it, were horrified. They'd been asked to choose between three options that differed in some details but all required the demolition of many homes and businesses to make way for a spacious paved walkway from the proposed site of the relocated train station entrance to the site of the new Tottenham Hotspur FC stadium, together with other proposed developments.

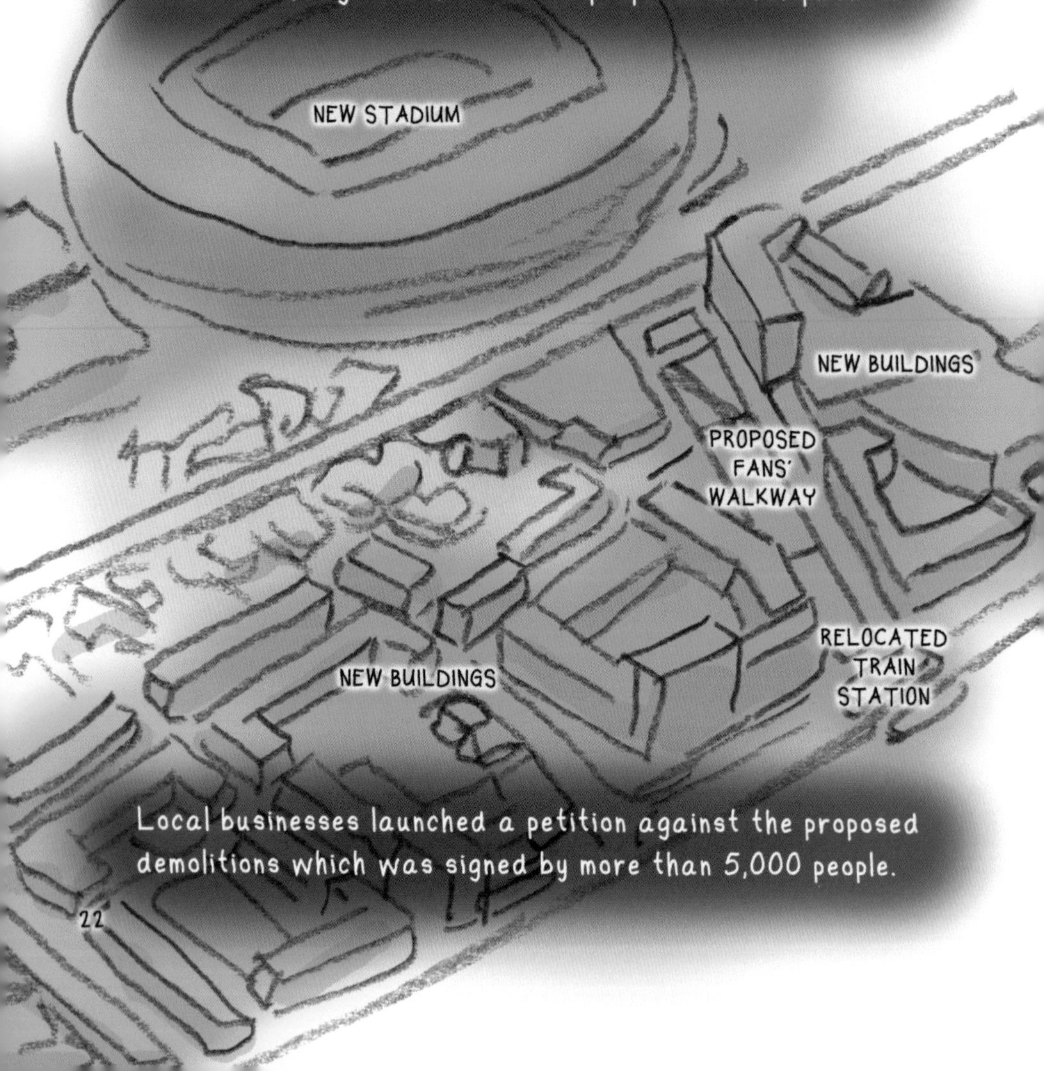

NEW STADIUM

NEW BUILDINGS

PROPOSED FANS' WALKWAY

RELOCATED TRAIN STATION

NEW BUILDINGS

Local businesses launched a petition against the proposed demolitions which was signed by more than 5,000 people.

When, why and how will you take us off the plan? We own our property.

Resident and Business Owner

Spurs Fan

They don't understand that consultation doesn't mean telling people what you've done after you've decided to do it.

...the kind of characterisation that somehow the council is dancing to Spurs' tune is something I find quite curious.

Councillor Claire Kober, Leader of Haringey Council

...maybe I shouldn't say this, but I think they should be knocked down, [the buildings] are an eye sore.

Haringey Councillor

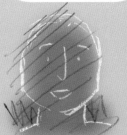

Executive, Tottenham Hotspur FC

It's not a walkway to the stadium, it's not our walkway.

Councillor Bull, Haringey

I just want to make sure this borough is not the patsy for Spurs. That's what I am concerned about, that's what I pick-up from the area forums and such-like and it just seems like everything is Spurs, Spurs, Spurs, Spurs, Spurs at the expense of everything else.

Haringey Council and Tottenham Hotspur FC said very little about the plans publicly. Neither organisation engaged with any of the residents or community groups in any meaningful way. A few Haringey councillors expressed reservations...

> You don't have to be close to the detail of the stadium plans or the wider place-changing agenda to be alarmed by what is proposed. Simply knowing that the plan involves bulldozing through shops on the High Road, council homes on the Love Lane Estate, and demolishing a public library for a fans' walkway tells you all you need to know about its social cleansing drive.

Councillor Bull, Haringey

However, the majority of Haringey Council was in favour of the plans. Those affected by the proposals became frustrated, they started to engage with the media and to draw attention to their plight. Dave Morris was interviewed on BBC Radio London.

> You see there will be some people who say that gentrification is a great thing, after all it makes their house prices go up for those who already own places.

> Well, the top priority is to serve the needs of local people throughout Tottenham and people are being forced out by high rents, high mortgages and lack of affordable housing. That's not acceptable.

Other Tottenham Residents were interviewed by David Conn for the Guardian Newspaper.

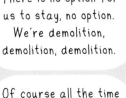

It's a good area why they want to move decent hard working people out of here I don't know.

There is no option for us to stay, no option. We're demolition, demolition, demolition.

Of course all the time you're thinking about it. Until the council have said where they are you can't fight anything.

This is prime land location. We are situated across the main entrance all right? Tottenham have been trying to own this for a long time.

Protest posters went up in the area that featured a cockerel and this caught the attention of Tottenham Hotspur FC's management. Adam Davison emailed Our Tottenham to invite some members to a meeting with Tottenham Hotspur FC executives on 4 July 2013 "to discuss the campaign and where there might be any areas of common ground. We certainly would welcome the opportunity to meet as we recognise the extremely important roles both organisations have to play in the renewal of Tottenham".

The members of the Our Tottenham network who attended the meeting came prepared. Dave Morris presented 7 points to the Tottenham Hotspur FC executives.

Point One: £100 million plus to be spent on the local community by Tottenham Hotspur, matching Arsenal's funding into the local community during it's own development.

Point Two: Tottenham Hotspur must not take public money for development schemes.

Point Three: No demolitions of homes and businesses.

Point Four: Improvements to homes and businesses to be funded by Tottenham Hotspur with no increase in rents for householders or businesses.

Point Five: At least 50% of all new homes built as part of the development and regeneration to be genuinely affordable social housing with permanent, secure tenancies.

Point Six: Improvements to existing community facilities e.g. libraries, GP surgeries, sports centres, community centres and youth clubs to be funded by Tottenham Hotspur.

Point Seven: Tottenham Hotspur to sign up to the Our Tottenham Community Charter.

Tottenham Hotspur FC executives expressed some concerns about copyright infringement on the cockerel posters. Perhaps that, and worries about potential damage to their reputation, were their main reasons for calling a meeting with the Our Tottenham network. Tottenham Hotspur executives denied responsibility for the walkway or any development schemes other than their stadium. They also said that Arsenal's funding could not be used as a comparison. Very little was achieved.

The direction of travel is wrong. Can we get a written response to the seven key points of our charter?

OK. As a club, the way we operate is to take as much of the community along with us as possible.

Dave Morris,
Tottenham Resident
and Community Activist

Donna-Maria Cullen,
Tottenham Hotspur

At the time of writing this book, almost four years later, Tottenham Hotspur FC have not replied to Our Tottenham's charter and there have been no further meetings between the two organisations. Tottenham residents and business owners have had to find other ways to express their concerns.

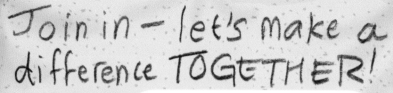

Many Tottenham Hotspur supporters became outraged by protests in the community and some of the terms in the Our Tottenham Community Charter - perhaps they felt that their new stadium was under threat.

They spoke about it online in the Tottenham and Wood Green Journal website and in Spurs fan forums. Though some had sympathy for the people of Tottenham...

As a Spurs fan I'd like to see Spurs pump in £100 million into this area. Time to give something back to the area from which it has taken so much... (and I'm not saying this as a resident of Tottenham).

I would rather Spurs give something back than buy big name signings. Truth is most locals and most people in general couldn't afford a ticket for White Hart Lane.

Others seemed to find it hard to understand that many of the people affected by the proposals had strong ties to Tottenham and might not be able to stay in the area - they would lose their homes and livelihoods.

Arsenal paid up and left! Spurs are committing to the area and they're a huge reason for the public cash being pumped into Tottenham. It's typical that we're just viewed as a cash cow by the locals rather than thanked for being the only thing keeping Haringey from drifting into oblivion.
The only two good things in Tottenham are Spurs itself and the Chick King. It is a horrendous place... I prefer watching on my sofa 4,000 miles away in Dubai.
The place is a shambles and I am too embarrassed to take clients there as things are at the moment.
Greedy little so and sos. How desperate do they sound trying to make it competitive that Spurs should go one better than Arsenal and give more money? Incredible.
N17 is a horrible area and residents should be grateful that a private enterprise deems it worthy to pump any money in at all. But, no, instead we're stuck with this redistribution of wealth nonsense.

In July 2014 Haringey Council held an event to celebrate its *Tottenham Strategic Regeneration Framework.* Some Haringey councillors attended but it seemed that they didn't understand the fears of people who would be most affected by the proposed changes.

We're the first people that will be transported out of Tottenham, and to many different places.

Love Lane Resident

I understand that demolition is incredibly difficult and traumatic but residents, on the whole, support the proposals.

Councillor Strickland,
Cabinet Member for Regeneration, Haringey

Tottenham is a wonderful community but it has some problems. Some parts lack opportunities and some have low educational results but the council is working hard to change these things.

Lyn Garner,
Director of Regeneration,
Planning and Development, Haringey

A crying ten-year-old whose family live above their shop asked...

Why is my home
being demolished?

Despite many people wanting to ask questions council
staff dimmed the lights to bring the meeting to a close.

The Our Tottenham network continued to grow and gain
strength; monthly meetings continued and there were two more
conferences. People, such as university students and planning
professionals, from within and outside the community were
beginning to take notice. Then a surprising meeting was held.

On 12 November 2014 Our Tottenham and other community groups met with the Tottenham Hotspur Supporters Trust and found they were in agreement over many issues: they overwhelmingly supported a new improved stadium and opposed inappropriate wider development such as the walkway between it and the relocated train station entrance.

It's not hard to see why the walkway is so controversial. It flies in the face of all the fine words about community benefit the club was so anxious to utter in the aftermath of the riots and symbolises the growing unease at the divide between private benefit and public good that colours much current debate.

Spurs Fan

A member of Our Tottenham expressed worries about the future.

There seems to be a huge mission creep. There is concern about the Tottenham Hotspur FC property arm buying up land and properties throughout the area. Are the overall regeneration plans really about stadium development to benefit fans and the team, or rather about property development and speculation?

Martin Cloake, Tottenham Hotspur Supporters' Trust board member, wrote after the meeting...

> More Spurs fans than some may imagine, certainly if the comments under the trust's last blog are anything to go by, are prepared to make common cause with the local community... For all the reported differences between Haringey Council and Tottenham Hotspur PLC over the years, it seems both organisations share a tendency to define consultation as "telling the punters what's been decided".

> Where once there was agreement and support across the board for a set of plans that seemed to deliver a better stadium that was part of a vibrant community, now there is suspicion and fear. What a sad failure that represents.

Tottenham Hotspur were still saying very little in public about the stadium and associated developments. Their legal action against Archway Sheet Metal Works, the family-run business situated on the site of the proposed new stadium, was ongoing. Despite the decision of the Planning Inspector, following hearings in 2013, that there was not a sufficiently compelling public interest case for the granting of a Compulsory Purchase Order, in July 2014 the Secretary of State for Communities and Local Government approved a Compulsory Purchase Order and Archway Metal put in an appeal.

Then on 25 November 2014 a fire broke out...

...gutting the Archway Metal building.

36

The fire started in the early hours of the morning. In newspaper reports the owners of Archway Metal said they had been receiving threats because of their refusal to move. There was mention of an investigation but the findings have not been made public and there have been no reports of the police taking any action.

Two months after the fire, on 20 February 2015, the High Court ruled against Archway Metal's appeal and granted a Compulsory Purchase Order to Haringey Council over the land the business had stood on.

The final piece of the land-assembly jigsaw puzzle was in place and it would now be possible for Tottenham Hotspur FC's new stadium to go ahead.

On 6 December 2014 Our Tottenham held a rally opposite the stadium to directly appeal to the Spurs fans who were there to see their team play against Crystal Palace. It was not a protest against the new stadium, it was to draw attention to the proposed fans' walkway and to other effects of regeneration plans in Haringey.

I hope Spurs fans will think about the Tottenham people who could lose their homes.

Over 5,000 people have signed the petition.

Spurs' stadium is being used as a Trojan horse for gentrification!

In June 2015 two members of Our Tottenham were invited to a meeting at Haringey Council and later received an email from Matthew Paterson, Head of Strategic Planning, Transport and Infrastructure. Matthew said he would review the draft Statement of Community Involvement to reflect some of their points and he would also address some problems with clarity in the information being given out to residents by Haringey. Small, but important gains, perhaps in recognition of the Our Tottenham network's increasing size and influence.

On 16 December Haringey granted further planning permission revisions to Tottenham Hotspur Football Club...

Community action

...for a redesigned stadium with capacity increased to 61,000 seats, a 180 bed hotel, a centre for extreme sports, a community medical centre and a new public square. The number of residential units were increased from 285 to 579, none of which will be classified as affordable housing.

Three locally listed buildings were deemed to be in the way of fans going to the new stadium. Campaigners lobbied the Mayor of London, Boris Johnson, to object to their demolition.

They were unsuccessful. In 2016 the buildings were demolished and some of the rubble will be displayed in a museum that is yet to be built.

On 22 May 2017 demolition began on Tottenham Hotspur FC's old stadium.

It was reported in July 2017 that Haringey Council had set aside £30.5 million to give to Tottenham Hotspur FC towards the cost of a raised public space next to the stadium and to purchase some of the club's land holdings in the area. It has also been reported that the football club asked Archway Metal, the business that had fought against moving, to make a time capsule to be buried at the point where the sites of the old and new stadiums overlap. It is not known if the commission was accepted.

The new stadium is due to open at the start of the 2018/19 football season and relocation of the White Hart Lane train station entrance will take place over a similar time-scale.

At the time of writing, demolition for the fans' walkway has not yet begun. Some residents have been moved from social housing in the Love Lane estate but many home and business owners remain. The Our Tottenham network, which includes local traders in the Tottenham Business Group and many other community groups, continues to challenge the plans for *High Road West* and other areas.

Since the Our Tottenham network was formed in 2013, there have been some benefits and achievements.

We give each other emotional support and we share our knowledge, resources and skills.

We've been able to slow the progress of Haringey's regeneration plans and we got some concessions.

Joining together as individuals and community groups in a network has given us more credibility and a bigger voice.

Though communities may feel powerless in the face of regeneration projects, the experience of the Our Tottenham network demonstrates that it is possible to make some impact on the process. The network gives encouragement and support, which allows people to speak out about their genuinely held views regarding the whole process of regeneration across the wider Tottenham area.

In addition to the fans' walkway and other proposals in Haringey there is a new challenge for the Our Tottenham network and others – The *Haringey Development Vehicle*. £2 billion of council owned assets is to be transferred into a public/private partnership with the developer Lend Lease. Proposals for this highly controversial plan include demolition of the Northumberland Park council housing estate plus many homes near the new Tottenham Hotspur FC stadium. The Haringey Civic Centre, a library in Wood Green, homes behind Shopping City as well as other housing estates and over 500 business units belonging to the council might also be demolished for private development. In 2017 campaigners organised two local marches, each over one thousand strong, and raised £25,000 through crowdfunding for a Judicial Review. Local campaigner Gordon Peters said...

There are implications of [the Judicial Review] which affect developments across London, and the rest of the country, as well as Haringey residents.

The proposed walkway in *High Road West* not only provides a link for fans from the relocated train station entrance to the new Tottenham Hotspur FC stadium it also connects the stadium to Haringey's further regeneration plans. It could be argued that these plans were triggered and led by the new stadium.

> We have national and regional government knocking on our doors, saying when are you going to build the stadium? The stadium is a catalyst for a ripple effect [of regeneration].

Executive, Tottenham Hotspur FC

Stadium-led regeneration is a complex issue, with many positives and negatives, some of which are hard to see until the stadium has been built. Many communities around the world have been affected by stadium-led regeneration and some of the positive legacies are not the ones that were stated or intended. Controversial stadium-led regeneration linked to the 2016 Rio Olympic Games sparked nation-wide protests involving tens of thousands of people and Brazil-based journalist Julia Michaels speaks of the way it has motivated a community.

> People in favelas are angry. I think the poor started to change the way they view themselves. They were empowered by this boom that included the Olympics. They are not as easily pushed off [to] the side as they were before, and it's going to be interesting to see how that plays out.

Developers and city planners often see stadium-led regeneration as a short cut to lifting an area out of its problems and fail to take into account potential negative consequences for existing communities.

This is a new problem and a new area of study, one that deserves more attention in order to reduce the negatives and encourage the benefits that can be derived from regeneration led by future stadiums.

47

Further information on groups and individuals mentioned in this book

Frederick Engels (1872) The Housing Question.
www.marxists.org/archive/marx/works/
1872/housing-question

Greater London Authority (2012)
It Took Another Riot. www.london.gov.uk/file/15966

Guardian (30.10.2013) Tottenham's new stadium:
how club can cash in on new development.
www.theguardian.com/football/2013/oct/30/
tottenham-new-stadium-local-business-demolition

Haringey Council www.haringey.gov.uk

(2012) A Plan for Tottenham.
www.haringey.gov.uk/sites/haringeygovuk/files/
a_plan_for_tottenham.pdf

(7.2.12) Report for Cabinet Item 12.
Funding and Investment Package for the Tottenham
Regeneration Program. www.minutes.haringey.gov.uk

(2013) High Road West consultation.
tottenham.london/HRWconsultation

(16.12.15) Report for Special Planning Sub-Committee.
www.minutes.haringey.gov.uk

Haringey Independent (15.9.14) Spurs fans, local people and businesses must stick together for a brighter future. www.haringeyindependent.co.uk/news/11519013.display

London Assembly (2015) The Regeneration Game. www.london.gov.uk/about-us/london-assembly/london-assembly-publications/regeneration-game

Julia Michaels riorealblog.com

Our Tottenham ourtottenham.org.uk

Mark Panton bbktheses.da.ulcc.ac.uk/260

Qin Shao history.tcnj.edu/faculty/qin-shao

Stop the HDV stophdv.com

Tottenham Hotspur FC www.tottenhamhotspur.com

Tottenham Hotspur Supporters Trust www.thstofficial.com

Tottenham and Wood Green Journal (05.05.13) Campaigners demand Spurs puts up 100 million for renewal of Tottenham

Mark Panton

After completing an MSc in Sport Management at Birkbeck College in 2011, Mark Panton joined the Birkbeck Sports Business Centre as a PhD student and recently obtained his doctorate from the University of London based on his research into the use of sport stadiums in urban regeneration projects. The research focused on the areas of Tottenham and East Manchester, specifically analysing the influence of local groups on these developments. In 2015 a number of his submissions were published in the London Assembly investigation into these issues for their *Regeneration Game* final report. As a qualified solicitor Mark maintains an interest in the legal aspects of sport, including the governance of sport organisations. His research interests also include the sociology of sport, the work of football community trusts and the influence of community groups. His outside interests have involved work as the secretary of the Dulwich Hamlet Supporters Trust; as research administrator for the Birkbeck TRIGGER project on gender in academia and roles with a number of not-for-profit organisations. Mark currently teaches on a number of courses at Birkbeck College.

For details of other places Mark has written or spoken about his work, please email m.panton@bbk.ac.uk Mark's thesis is available at bbktheses.da.ulcc.ac.uk/260